Topic 1

Tectonic processes and hazards

Why are some locations more at risk from tectonic hazards?

The global distribution of tectonic hazards

Hazards are natural events that have an adverse impact on people, the economy and society. Tectonic hazards include earthquakes and volcanic eruptions, as well as secondary hazards such as tsunamis. The global distribution of these hazards is largely explained by the pattern of plate boundaries and their tectonic processes.

1 What is meant by a *plate boundary?* 　　　　　　　　　　　`2 marks`

....

....

....

2 Name the FOUR types of plate boundary. 　　　　　　　　　　`4 marks`

....

....

....

....

3 Identify the TWO plate boundaries where the most powerful earthquakes occur. 　`2 marks`

....

....

....

4 Identify the TWO plate boundaries where most volcanoes occur. 　　　`2 marks`

....

....

....

5 What are *hotspot volcanoes* and where do they occur? 　　　　　　`4 marks`

....

....

....

....

....

6 Describe the origins of the Mid-Atlantic Ridge and its associated tectonic hazards. `6 marks`

....

....

....

....

....

7 Why are some locations more at risk from tectonic hazards than others? `3 marks`

....

....

....

The theory of plate tectonics

This theory was developed more than 60 years ago. It draws together a range of evidence supporting the idea that the Earth's crust is made up of great slabs of two different types of crust. The evidence includes fold mountains, sea-floor spreading, the topography of the ocean floors, paleo-magnetism and the locations of earthquakes and volcanoes. The theory also helps to explain the processes at work along plate margins and the magnitude of associated tectonic events.

8 Distinguish between the TWO different types of the Earth's crust. `4 marks`

....

....

....

....

9 What causes tectonic plates to move? `1 mark`

....

10 Name THREE processes at work along a destructive plate boundary. `3 marks`

....

....

....

11 What is *paleo-magnetism* and how does it help in the study of plate tectonics? `4 marks`

....

....

....

....

....

12 What is a *locked fault* and why is it a cause for concern? 6 marks

....

....

....

....

....

....

....

13 What is the *Benioff Zone*? 4 marks

....

....

....

....

Physical processes and tectonic hazards

Physical processes at plate boundaries largely explain the locations, causes and hazardous outcomes of earthquakes and volcanic eruptions. Tsunamis are more commonly caused by earthquakes, but their hazardous impacts can be far more widespread and just as devastating. Each of these three types of tectonic events can vary enormously in their magnitude.

14 Distinguish between the *hypocentre* and *epicentre* of an earthquake. 3 marks

....

....

....

....

15 Distinguish between the *magnitude* and *intensity* of an earthquake. 3 marks

....

....

....

16 Describe the THREE different types of seismic wave. 3 marks

....

....

....

....

17 Describe ONE secondary hazard associated with earthquakes. 2 marks

....

....

....

18 Name THREE primary volcanic hazards and describe how each threatens people. 3 marks

....

....

....

....

....

....

19 What are *jökulhaups* and why are they hazardous? 2 marks

....

....

....

....

20 Study Figure 1. Describe and explain the distribution of notable tsunami events. 6 marks

Key
● Historic tsunami event

Figure 1

....

Why do some tectonic hazards develop into disasters?

Tectonic hazards become tectonic disasters

The reason why some tectonic hazards become disasters is linked to three factors:
- the magnitude of the tectonic event
- its location relative to densely populated areas
- the exposure or vulnerability of people in the affected area, and their resilience in coping with the impacts of the hazard

21 **What is meant by *vulnerability* in the context of hazards?** `2 marks`

....

....

22 **What is meant by *resilience* in the context of hazards?** `2 marks`

....

....

23 **What is the *hazard-risk equation*?** `1 mark`

....

....

24 **What makes a hazard into a disaster?** `3 marks`

....

....

....

....

25 **Name the TWO pressures in the Pressure and Release model.** `2 marks`

....

....

26 Outline what you consider to be the main economic impacts of tectonic hazards. `4 marks`

....

....

....

....

27 Explain the possible link between the capacity of a country to cope with a hazard and its level of development. `6 marks`

....

....

....

....

....

....

....

28 Why are the impacts of earthquakes generally greater than those of volcanoes? Give your reasons. `4 marks`

....

....

....

....

....

Tectonic hazard profiles

Hazard profiles are used to understand and compare the physical characteristics and processes of the three different types of tectonic hazard. They are also used to compare the same type of hazard event in different locations and at different times. These profiles are of value to those decision makers involved in the day-to-day management of hazards.

29 Name TWO of the scales used to measure the magnitude and intensity of earthquakes. `2 marks`

....

....

30 How do your two scales differ? `4 marks`

....

....

....

....

....

31 What does *VEI* stand for, and what exactly does it measure? *(4 marks)*

....

....

....

....

....

32 Name the SIX characteristics commonly used in producing a tectonic hazard profile. *(3 marks)*

....

....

....

....

....

33 Explain the value of compiling hazard profiles. *(4 marks)*

....

....

....

....

....

....

Development, governance and disaster impacts

The level of development and the quality of governance are important in understanding a significant aspect of tectonic hazards, namely the vulnerability of people and their ability to survive the impacts. A high level of vulnerability and a lack of resilience can turn a hazard into a disaster. This is where the level of development and the quality of governance come into play as key factors. In short, a developed country with good governance is likely to be better prepared and better able to cope with the impacts of a hazard event.

34 Identify the inequalities that make low-income households and communities carry a disproportionate share of disaster 'costs'. *(4 marks)*

....

....

....

....

....

35 In what ways does poor governance increase vulnerability to the impacts of tectonic hazards?

4 marks

....

....

....

....

....

36 Identify the factors that made ONE specific earthquake event into a disaster.

4 marks

....

....

....

....

....

37 Identify TWO ways in which disasters can create development opportunities.

4 marks

....

....

....

....

38 Study Table 1 which shows the number of people reported killed and affected by tectonic hazards between 2004 and 2013. Countries are grouped according to their level of human development (HD).

Table 1

Tectonic risk	Very high HD	High HD	Medium HD	Low HD	Total
Earthquakes and tsunamis	21,036	38,019	293,941	297,328	650,321
Volcanic eruptions	0	21	330	12	363
Earthquakes and tsunamis	4,010,000	2,476,000	67,972,000	9,495,000	83,953,000
Volcanic eruptions	12,000	348,000	568,000	323,000	1,215,000

Red = killed; orange = affected

What conclusions do you draw from the table about the relationship between the human impacts of tectonic hazards and level of development?

6 marks

....

....

....

....

....

....

How successful is the management of tectonic hazards and disasters?

Understanding recent hazard and disaster trends

Over the last 50 years, the total number of all hazards (not just tectonic) has increased, while the number of reported disasters and deaths has fallen. But the economic costs of hazards and disasters of all types have risen considerably. These trends convey a mixed message when it comes to evaluating the quality of hazard management.

39 Give reasons why disaster statistics are not altogether reliable. `4 marks`

....

....

....

....

40 Spatial scale is ONE characteristic of a mega-disaster. Outline other characteristics. `4 marks`

....

....

....

....

41 Give ONE recent example of a tectonic mega-disaster. `1 mark`

....

42 What is a *multiple-hazard zone*? Name ONE country that is particularly exposed to multiple hazards. `2 marks`

....

....

43 Give an example of how different types of natural hazard may be linked. `2 marks`

....

....

....

44 Explain why there is concern about the world's rapidly-growing mega-cities. `6 marks`

....

....

....

....

....

....

Managing tectonic hazards (1)

Two of the most obvious approaches to the management of tectonic hazards involve:

- improving the prediction or forecasting of hazard events

- raising the general level of preparedness for hazards, for example, through education and having rehearsed emergency procedures

45 **Name the FOUR main stages in the hazard management cycle.** (4 marks)

....

....

....

46 **What does the risk disk model attempt to explain?** (3 marks)

....

....

....

....

47 **Explain the role of scientists as players when dealing with tectonic hazards.** (4 marks)

....

....

....

....

....

48 **Give THREE examples of the human factors affecting the response to a tectonic hazard.** (3 marks)

....

....

....

49 **Identify the FOUR stages in Park's model of the disaster response curve.** (4 marks)

....

....

....

50 **Describe how the Park's model can help in the study of tectonic disasters.** (6 marks)

....

....

....

....

....

....

Managing tectonic hazards (2)

Managing the impacts of tectonic hazards can be achieved by mitigation (sometimes referred to as adaptation or preparation). Increasing technology allows the potential impacts of a hazard to be mitigated by making more effective adaptations. First the focus is on losses, then on vulnerability and resilience. In a few instances, even the causes of the hazard might be targeted.

51 **What is a *mitigation strategy*?** 2 marks

....

....

....

....

52 **Give ONE example of a micro approach to improving protection from each of the following hazard events:** 2 marks

a **earthquakes**

....

b **volcanoes**

....

53 **Give TWO examples of a macro approach to improving protection from tsunamis.** 2 marks

....

....

....

....

54 **Describe the roles of the following players in managing the impacts of tectonic hazards:** 6 marks

a **planners**

....

....

....

....

b **insurers**

....

....

....

....

c **non-government organisations (NGOs)**

....

....

....

....

55 **Identify the FOUR priorities of the Sendai Framework for Action (2015).** 4 marks

....

....

....

....

....

....

....

56 **Study Figure 2 which shows the number of hazard loss events between 1980 and 2014.**

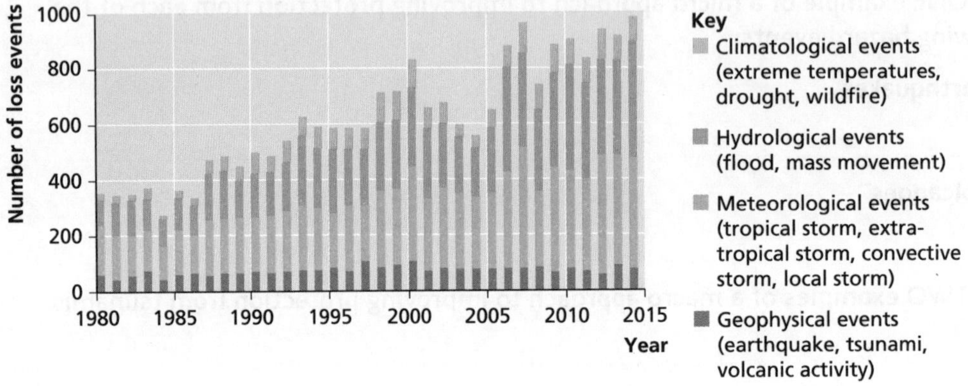

Number of loss events
1000
800
600
400
200
0
1980
1985
1990
1995
2000
2005
2010
2015
Year
Key
Climatological events (extreme temperatures, drought, wildfire)
Hydrological events (flood, mass movement)
Meteorological events (tropical storm, extra-tropical storm, convective storm, local storm)
Geophysical events (earthquake, tsunami, volcanic activity)

Figure 2

What conclusions do you draw about geophysical (tectonic) hazards relative to other types of hazard? 6 marks

....

....

....

....

....

....

....

....

....

....

....

....

....

....

....

....

Exam-style questions

1 Study Figure 3 which compares volcanic eruptions with other types of natural hazard.

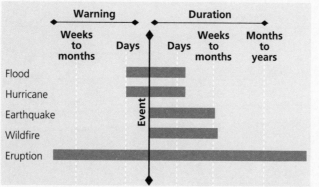

Source: www.volcano.gov

Are volcanic eruptions a unique natural hazard? Explain the reasons for your answer.

5-8   **6 marks**

....

....

....

....

....

....

....

....

2 Explain why some tectonic disasters are more costly than others.

12-15   **12 marks**

....

....

....

....

....

....

....

....

....

....

....

....

....

3 Evaluate the four different approaches to hazard management. ⏱ 25 · **20 marks**

Topic 2A

Glaciated landscapes and change

How has climate change influenced the formation of glaciated landscapes?

The causes of climate change

Although the Pleistocene was a period of global cooling and widespread continental glaciation, within it there were multiple periods of warmer conditions (interglacials). During the warmer Quaternary epoch that has followed — the Holocene — there have been many short-term fluctuations in climate. The causes of these periods of global cooling have ranged from variations in the Earth's axis and in the composition of its atmosphere to plate tectonics and sunspot activity.

① How many significant glacials were there during the Pleistocene period?   1 mark

② Name the THREE main characteristics of the Earth's orbit that are an important part of Milankovitch's theory.   3 marks

③ Give ONE piece of evidence that supports Milankovitch's theory.   1 mark

④ Explain what is meant by the *climate feedback mechanism*.   4 marks

⑤ What is the term given to the short-term oscillations in climate within glacial and interglacial periods?   1 mark

⑥ Name and explain ONE possible cause of these oscillations.   4 marks

7 With reference to the Little Ice Age: 6 marks

    a State roughly when it occurred.

....

....

    b Outline the evidence for its occurrence.

....

....

....

....

Past and present distributions of ice cover

The cryosphere consists of ice sheets and glaciers, together with sea and lake ice, ground ice (permafrost) and snow cover. Mass and energy are constantly being exchanged between the cryosphere and other major components of the Earth, namely the lithosphere, hydrosphere, atmosphere and biosphere. It is the variations in these exchanges that cause the cryosphere to expand and contract, thereby changing the global distribution of ice cover.

8 Distinguish between:

    a an *ice sheet* and an *ice field*   3 marks

....

....

....

    b a *valley glacier* and a *piedmont glacier*   3 marks

....

....

....

9 Explain the significance of distinguishing between *warm-based* and *cold-based* glaciers.   6 marks

....

....

....

....

....

....

10 Identify the FOUR main factors affecting the global distribution of ice cover. `2 marks`

....

....

....

11 a What percentage of the Earth's land area is covered by glaciers today? `1 mark`

....

b What was the approximate percentage at the height of the Pleistocene glaciation? `1 mark`

....

12 Describe TWO ways in which the global distribution of ice cover in the late Pleistocene differed from that today. `4 marks`

....

....

....

13 What is the evidence for the differences you described in question 12? `4 marks`

....

....

....

....

....

Periglacial processes and their landscapes

The term periglacial was originally used to refer to the climate conditions and landscapes that characterised the areas near the margins of Pleistocene glaciers and ice sheets. Today, however, the term is more widely used to include all high altitude or high latitude areas with cold climates and land that may or may not have been glaciated.

14 Define the following terms: `2 marks`

a *permafrost*

....

....

b *active layer*

....

....

15 Explain how TWO factors, other than climate, influence the distribution and
character of permafrost on a local scale?   4 marks

....

....

....

....

16 Name FOUR basic periglacial processes.   4 marks

....

....

....

....

17 List THREE possible relict periglacial landforms found in Great Britain, and outline
how they were formed.   6 marks

....

....

....

....

....

....

....

18 Where are most of these relict features found in Great Britain, and why? 2 marks

....

....

19 Study Figure 4 which shows the climate at a periglacial location.

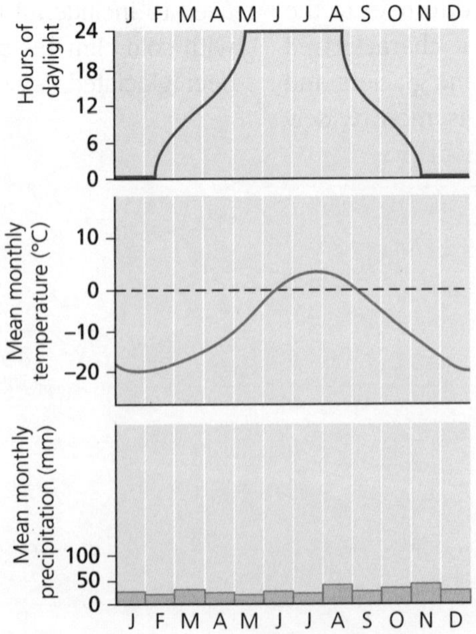

Figure 4

Describe the characteristics of the climate at this location.   6 marks

....

....

....

....

....

What processes operate within glacier systems?

The operation of glaciers as systems

To understand how glaciers behave, it is helpful to view them as systems with inputs and outputs as well as interacting with other Earth systems. Mass balance relates to the relationship between the glacier's inputs (accumulation) and outputs (ablation). Accumulation tends to be greater than ablation in the upper part of a glacier, while the relationship is reversed in the lower part.

20 What are the inputs to a glacier?   2 marks

....

....

21 What are the outputs of a glacier?   2 marks

....

....

22 What is the *equilibrium point* of a glacier?   2 marks

....

....

23 Explain why glaciers are dynamic systems.   6 marks

....

....

....

....

....

....

....

24 Explain the significance of a glacier's energy budget in the long term. 3 marks

....

....

25 Describe THREE ways in which satellites are helping the study of ice sheets in remote locations. 6 marks

....

....

....

....

....

Explaining glacial movement and rate variations

The basic cause of ice movement is gravity. Ice moves downslope from higher altitudes to either lower locations on land or to sea level. The greater the accumulation of snow and ice, the stronger the force of gravity. The rate of downslope movement also depends on the interplay of other factors.

26 Why do polar and temperate glaciers move at different rates? 3 marks

....

....

27 Describe the THREE processes that are important to glacier movement. 6 marks

....

....

....

....

28 Outline the factors affecting the rate of glacier movement. 6 marks

....

....

....

....

....

29 What is meant by a *glacial surge*? `3 marks`

The glacier landform system

The ability of a glacier or ice sheet to change the landscape depends to a large extent on its speed of movement. The greater the speed, the more debris is picked up and transported. It is this debris that provides the grinding that is an essential part of erosion. The erosion takes place at the ice base and, in the case of glaciers, on the valley sides.

30 Describe the FOUR main glacial processes of the glacier system. `4 marks`

31 Give ONE example of a glacial landform at each of the following scales: `3 marks`

a macro

b meso

c micro

32 Give the location of each of the following glacier process environments: `5 marks`

a subglacial

b englacial

c marginal

d proglacial

e periglacial

33 Explain the general difference between upland and lowland glaciated landscapes. 2 marks

....

....

....

34 Study Figure 5 which shows the intensity of glacial erosion in Britain during part of the Pleistocene.

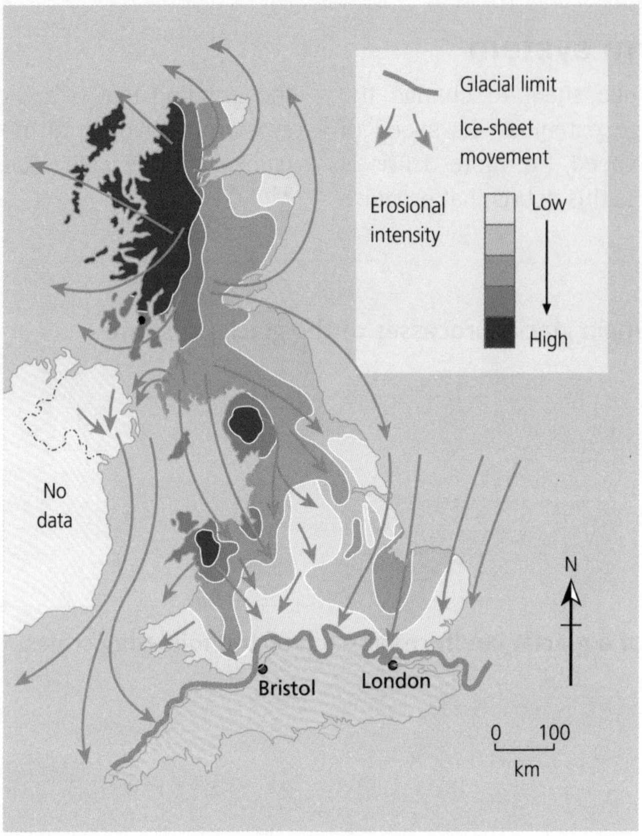

Figure 5

Describe the distribution of erosional intensity and suggest reasons for the spatial variations. 6 marks

....

....

....

....

....

....

....

....

....

....

....

....

How do glacial processes contribute to the formation of glacial landforms and landscapes?

Glacial erosion and the glaciated landscape

The most important factor determining the efficiency of glacial erosion is the size of the glacier — its thickness and thermal regime. Velocity of movement is another vital factor and was discussed earlier. Generally speaking, glacial erosion operates more effectively when the glacier ice is warm-based and there is abundant meltwater and debris being transported.

35 **Distinguish between at least THREE different glacial erosion processes.** `3 marks`

....

....

....

36 **Name TWO other processes that combine with glacial erosion to make it more effective.** `2 marks`

....

....

37 **Draw an annotated diagram to show the formation of a cirque.** `6 marks`

38 **Explain the link between cirques, pyramidal peaks and arêtes.** `4 marks`

....

....

....

....

39 **Describe the landforms associated with glacial troughs.** `4 marks`

....

....

....

....

40 Explain what is meant by the term *ice-sheet scouring*. `2 marks`

41 With reference to specific landforms resulting from ice-sheet scouring, show how differential geology is an important factor in their formation. `6 marks`

Landforms and landscapes of glacial deposition

The main processes of glacial deposition are lodgement, ablation, deformation and flow. Moraine is the term used to refer to an accumulation of glacial debris, whether it is dumped by an active glacier or left behind as a deposit after glacial retreat. Glacial deposition should not be confused with fluvioglacial deposition undertaken by glacial meltwater.

42 Explain what is meant by *ice-contact depositional features*. `2 marks`

43 Distinguish between a *terminal moraine* and a *recessional moraine*. `3 marks`

44 Explain how drumlins are thought to have been formed. `4 marks`

45 *Lodgement till* is also known by what other term? `1 mark`

46 Describe THREE lowland glacial deposition features. `3 marks`

47 Explain how the extent and direction of ice movement can be reconstructed from an examination of glacial depositional features. `6 marks`

Glacial meltwater

Glacial meltwater comes from two sources: surface melting and basal melting. It plays an important part in the processes of erosion, transport and deposition. It is directly involved in glacier movement providing the lubrication need for basal sliding. It is also responsible for some erosion of the valley floor beneath the glacier. It is indirectly involved in the processes of glacial abrasion and plucking.

48 Name the TWO types of melting taking place in or on a glacier. `2 marks`

49 Name the THREE types of glacial meltwater flow. `3 marks`

50 Describe the ways in which fluvioglacial deposits differ from glacial deposits. `6 marks`

51 Explain the difference between ice-contact and proglacial fluvioglacial landforms.

6 marks

....

....

....

....

....

....

....

....

....

52 Study Figure 6 which is a rose diagram (polar graph) showing the results of pebble orientation in a Scottish lowland glacial deposit.

Figure 6

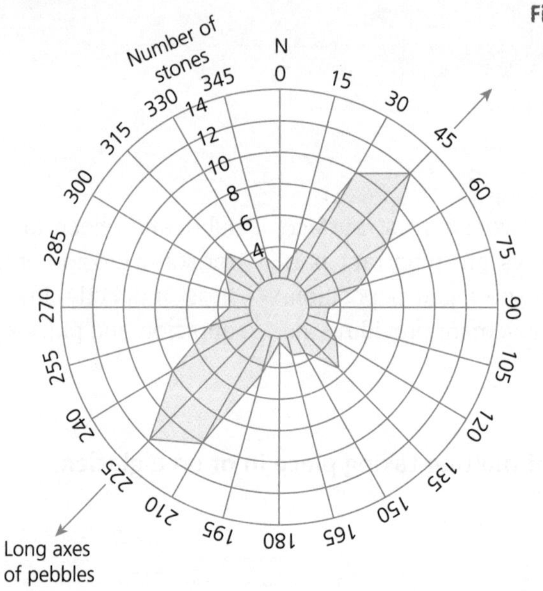

What does the diagram tells us about the direction of ice movement?

6 marks

....

....

....

....

....

....

....

....

How are glaciated landscapes used and managed today?

The value of glacial and periglacial landscapes

It is necessary to draw a distinction between the active glacial and periglacial landscapes found today at high latitudes and altitudes, and relict glaciated landscapes. Whereas most of the former are likely to be classified as wilderness, the latter are less likely due to the presence of people and economic development.

53 What is the difference between a *glacial* and a *glaciated* environment? `2 marks`

54 Suggest a definition of:

a *wilderness* `1 mark`

b *wilderness continuum* `2 marks`

55 Outline the range of attitudes that exist towards active glacial landscapes. `4 marks`

56 Examine the potential economic value of glaciated areas. `6 marks`

57 It is said that glacial and periglacial areas are of great ecological and environmental value. Give some examples of this value. `6 marks`

The threats facing glaciated landscapes

Glaciated areas are threatened to some extent by natural hazards. They in turn threaten people and their settlements. However, the main threats come from a range of human activities. These result in the disfigurement of fine natural scenery, the pollution of air and water, as well as the degradation of ecosystems.

59 Name TWO natural hazards that occur in glaciated areas. `2 marks`

....

....

60 Name THREE human threats to glaciated areas. `3 marks`

....

....

....

61 Identify human activities that degrade the landscape and ecosystems. `4 marks`

....

....

....

....

....

62 Identify players whose actions are reducing the resilience of glaciated upland landscapes. `4 marks`

....

....

....

....

....

63 Outline TWO impacts that global warming is having on glacier systems. `4 marks`

....

....

....

....

....

64 Who are the players who are *indirectly* altering the natural systems of glacial and glaciated landscapes? `4 marks`

....

....

....

....

....

Approaches to managing the threats facing glacial and glaciated landscapes

Possible approaches range from 'do nothing' or 'business as usual' to 'total protection'. In between, there are at least three different management strategies:

- sustainable exploitation of resources
- sustainable management
- comprehensive conservation

The gradient between these three intermediate management objectives is one of increasing resistance to anything that might threaten glacial and glaciated landscapes.

65 **Identify the major stakeholders in glacial areas.** `3 marks`

66 **Explain Antarctica's unique system of international governance.** `4 marks`

67 **Give examples of actions at a national level aimed at protecting glacial and glaciated landscapes.** `4 marks`

68 **Give some examples of the ways in which climate warming is challenging glacial environments.** `4 marks`

69 **Explain why global warming is creating an uncertain future in glacial areas.** `3 marks`

70 Suggest what might be done by way of mitigation and adaptation. 4 marks

....

....

....

71 Study Figure 7 which shows some different opinions about the Antarctic Treaty System (ATS).

Figure 7

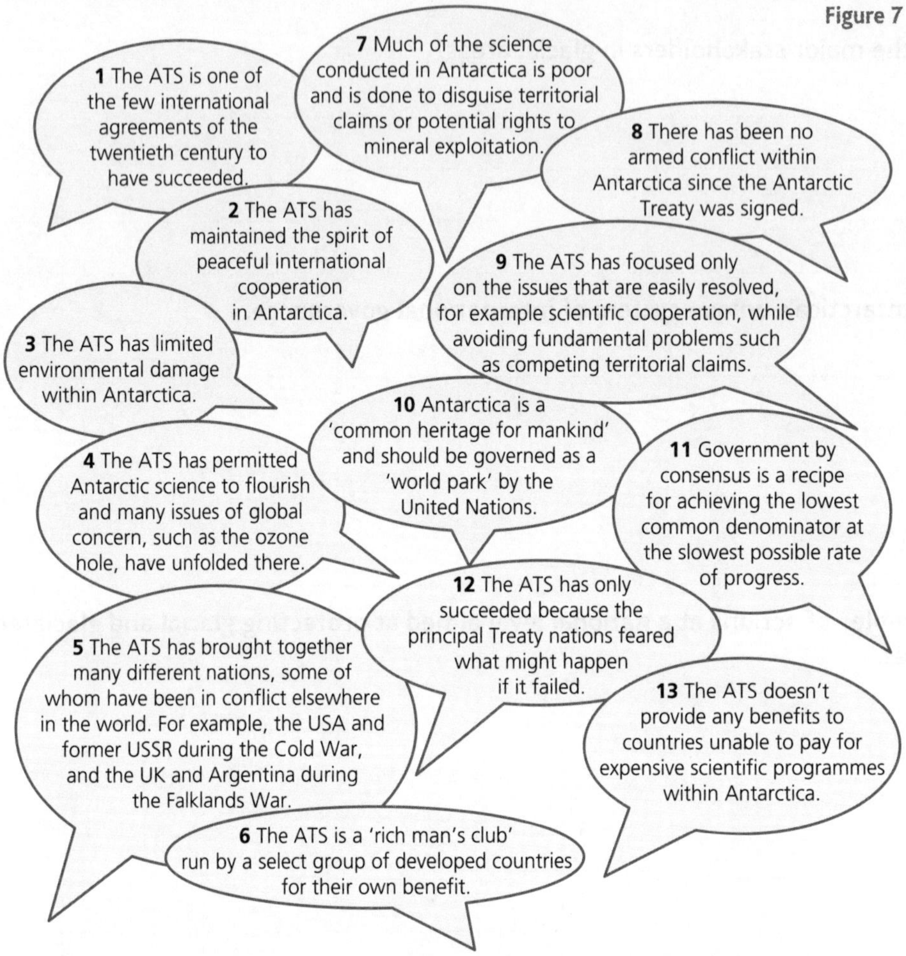

1 The ATS is one of the few international agreements of the twentieth century to have succeeded.

2 The ATS has maintained the spirit of peaceful international cooperation in Antarctica.

3 The ATS has limited environmental damage within Antarctica.

4 The ATS has permitted Antarctic science to flourish and many issues of global concern, such as the ozone hole, have unfolded there.

5 The ATS has brought together many different nations, some of whom have been in conflict elsewhere in the world. For example, the USA and former USSR during the Cold War, and the UK and Argentina during the Falklands War.

6 The ATS is a 'rich man's club' run by a select group of developed countries for their own benefit.

7 Much of the science conducted in Antarctica is poor and is done to disguise territorial claims or potential rights to mineral exploitation.

8 There has been no armed conflict within Antarctica since the Antarctic Treaty was signed.

9 The ATS has focused only on the issues that are easily resolved, for example scientific cooperation, while avoiding fundamental problems such as competing territorial claims.

10 Antarctica is a 'common heritage for mankind' and should be governed as a 'world park' by the United Nations.

11 Government by consensus is a recipe for achieving the lowest common denominator at the slowest possible rate of progress.

12 The ATS has only succeeded because the principal Treaty nations feared what might happen if it failed.

13 The ATS doesn't provide any benefits to countries unable to pay for expensive scientific programmes within Antarctica.

Which of the opinions do you:

a support most?

....

b support least?

....

Give your reasons in both instances. 6 marks

....

....

....

....

....

Exam-style questions

Figure 8

1 Study Figure 8 which shows a glaciated landform in the UK. Identify the landform and explain how it was formed.

6-8   6 marks

....

....

....

....

....

....

2 Assess the importance of glacial meltwater in the glacial landscape.

10-12   12 marks

....

....

....

....

....

....

....

....

....

....

....

....

....

....

....

....

3 Evaluate the economic value of glaciated landscapes.

25 20 marks

Topic 2B

Coastal landscapes and change

Why are coastal landscapes different and what processes cause these differences?

Distinctive features and landscapes of the coast and the littoral zone

The coast represents the boundary where land and sea meet, and where both marine and terrestrial processes operate and interact. The littoral zone consists of four subzones: the coast, the backshore, the nearshore and the offshore. It contains a wide variety of coastal landscapes produced by the interaction of wind, waves and currents, as well as sediment from terrestrial and offshore sources. It is a highly dynamic zone of often rapid change.

1 Describe the essential features of the backshore. `3 marks`

....

....

....

2 Describe the essential features of the nearshore. `2 marks`

....

....

3 Suggest THREE different criteria that might be used in classifying coasts. `6 marks`

....

....

....

....

....

....

....

....

....

4 What are *subaerial processes*? `3 marks`

....

....

....

35

5 Describe the essential features of coastal plains. 3 marks

....

....

....

6 Contrast the profiles of two high-relief cliffs — one which is being actively eroded and the other not. 6 marks

....

....

....

....

....

....

....

....

The influence of geological structure on coastal landscapes

Geological structure refers to the arrangement of rocks in three dimensions and to three key elements: strata (different layers of rock); deformation (degree of tilting or folding), and faulting (fractures causing rocks to be displaced from their original positions). These three elements of geological structure influence coastal landscapes, often as much as lithology (rock type).

7 What is the difference between a *concordant coast* and a *discordant coast*? 4 marks

....

....

....

....

8 Name an example of each type of coast. 2 marks

....

....

9 Explain what a *Haff coastline* is. 3 marks

....

....

....

10 Headlands and bays are a feature of discordant coasts. Explain why marine processes gradually smooth out such coasts. **6 marks**

....
....
....
....
....
....
....
....
....
....

11 Examine the influence of dip on cliff profiles. **6 marks**

....
....
....
....
....
....
....
....
....
....

12 What are the micro-features of a cliff and how are they formed? **3 marks**

....
....
....
....
....
....

Rates of coastal recession

Rates of coastal erosion and coastal recession are important aspects of the dynamic coast. They are crucial facts that should be fully known in drawing up any scheme of coastal management. These rates are determined by many factors, but the key one is lithology or rock type. Another significant factor is vegetation, particularly the degree of cover and general resistance to the forces of coastal erosion.

13 Complete the table below about the rates of erosion of different rock types. `6 marks`

Rock type	Examples	Erosion rate	Explanation
Igneous			
Metamorphic			
Sedimentary			

14 Describe how the differential erosion of alternating and contrasting rocks affects the coastline. `4 marks`

....

....

....

....

15 Explain why vegetation is a factor affecting coastal recession. `4 marks`

....

....

....

....

16 Explain why estuaries are ideal for the development of salt marshes. `6 marks`

....

....

....

....

....

....

....

17 Study Figure 9 which shows the plant succession along a cross-section of sand dunes.

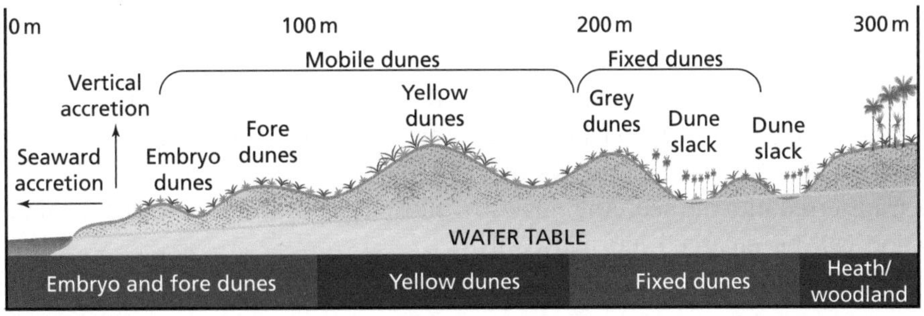

Figure 9

a **Explain the formation of each of the following:** `4 marks`

   i **embryo dunes**

   ....

   ....

   ....

   ....

   ii **dune slacks**

   ....

   ....

   ....

   ....

b **Apart from colour, what distinguishes yellow dunes from grey dunes?** `2 marks`

   ....

   ....

   ....

   ....

   ....

c **Why is marram grass so important to the formation of sand dunes?** `4 marks`

   ....

   ....

   ....

   ....

   ....

   ....

   ....

How do characteristic coastal landforms contribute to coastal landscapes?

Coastal landforms created by marine erosion

Waves are an essential part of marine erosion, transport and deposition. They are caused by friction between the wind and the sea surface. The contact allows the wind's energy to be transferred into the sea. Any ripples created by this friction can be enlarged into waves if the wind is sustained or strengthens. Out at sea, waves are just energy moving through the water. The water itself simply moves up and down, with some orbital movement of water particles within each wave.

18 **What is the difference between *tides* and *currents*?** `4 marks`

19 **Describe what happens to waves when they reach shallow water.** `3 marks`

20 **Distinguish between *constructive waves* and *destructive waves*.** `6 marks`

21 a What is the difference between *hydraulic action* and *corrosion*? `3 marks`

....

....

....

....

b Name TWO other marine erosion processes. `2 marks`

....

....

22 Describe the suite of coastal landforms most commonly found in areas of sedimentary rock with defined bedding planes and joints. `3 marks`

....

....

....

....

Coastal landforms created by sediment transport and deposition

Material eroded from cliffs is transported by the sea as sediment. There are different modes of transport. The movement of sediment is rarely seaward and landward, but rather it is moved along the coast by currents. The transport along the coast tends to take place within sediment cells in which both erosion and deposition are taking place.

23 Suspension and solution are two processes by which sediment is transported. Name and define the other TWO processes. `4 marks`

....

....

....

....

24 What is *longshore drift*? `4 marks`

....

....

....

....

....

....

25 Explain how each of the following depositional features is formed: **6 marks**

a   tombolo

....

....

....

....

....

b   recurved spit

....

....

....

....

....

c   cuspate foreland

....

....

....

....

....

26 Examine the factors affecting the stability of depositional features. **4 marks**

....

....

....

....

....

....

27 What are *sediment* or *littoral* cells? **4 marks**

....

....

....

....

....

....

....

....

Subaerial processes and coastal landforms

Weathering is important in the production of sediment and the role of mass movement is to transfer that terrestrial material into the sea. They are both significant factors affecting the rate of coastal recession.

Both processes create distinctive landforms and, as a consequence, contribute to the appearance of coastal landscapes.

28 **Describe the THREE types of weathering.** 6 marks

....

....

....

....

....

....

29 **What is *mass movement*?** 2 marks

....

....

....

30 **Describe THREE different types of mass movement.** 6 marks

....

....

....

....

....

....

31 **Describe the effects of mass movement on the coastal landscape.** 3 marks

....

....

....

32 **What is the link between subaerial processes and rates of coastal recession?** 4 marks

....

....

....

....

....

....

33 Study Figure 10 which shows the relationship between climate and weathering.

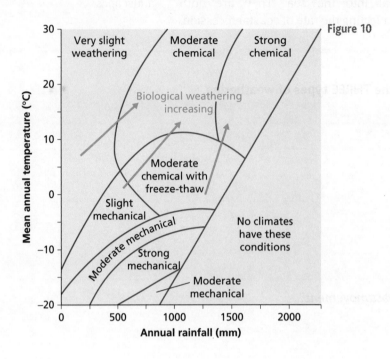

Figure 10

a   Explain the increase in biological weathering.   2 marks

....

....

....

....

....

b   Compare cold and hot climates in terms of weathering.   3 marks

....

....

....

....

....

c   Where in the world do you think that coastal landforms are most affected by
    subaerial processes? Give your reasons.   3 marks

....

....

....

....

....

....

How do coastal erosion and sea level change alter the physical characteristics of coastlines and increase risks?

Sea level change and the coast

Changes in sea level influence the coast on different time scales. Those changes range from daily, small-scale tidal movements to substantial shifts in mean sea level over thousands of years, as happened during the Pleistocene. Perhaps in between those extremes, we have the rising sea level caused by current global warming. Longer-term sea level changes can have a powerful influence on the coastal landscape.

34 What is the difference between an *isostatic* change and a *eustatic* change in sea level? **4 marks**

35 What might be the cause of an isostatic: **4 marks**

a rise in sea level?

b fall in sea level?

36 What type of coastline results from a eustatic fall in sea level? **1 mark**

37 What are the coastal features created by a rising sea level? **4 marks**

38 Explain why it is difficult to predict future sea levels with any accuracy. **4 marks**

39 Describe how tectonic activity can affect sea level. `4 marks`

....

....

....

....

The threats of rapid coastal retreat

Rising sea levels can pose a particular threat to people living in coastal zones. They do so because they can be a factor helping to accelerate coastal retreat. The challenge is made worse by the huge numbers of people living on or near the coast. Many of the world's largest cities have coastal locations and much of the world's economic wealth is generated and concentrated in the coastal zone.

40 List FOUR physical factors that encourage coastal recession. `4 marks`

....

....

....

....

41 Explain why dredging can increase coastal erosion. `3 marks`

....

....

42 Give an example and an explanation of 'dams that cause coastal erosion'. `4 marks`

....

....

....

....

43 Explain how weathering and mass movement contribute to coastal recession. `2 marks`

....

....

44 Why do rates of coastal recession vary over time? `4 marks`

....

....

....

45 How is modern technology helping to measure coastal erosion? `4 marks`

The risk of coastal flooding

Coastal flooding is an increasingly significant risk along some coasts. The risk is heightened by the fact that such a large proportion of the world's population lives and works only a few metres above present sea level, for example along coastal plains, around estuaries and on huge river deltas. Such areas are menaced by storm surges that seem to be increasing in frequency and devastation.

46 Name TWO megadeltas which contain large populations. `2 marks`

47 What is a *storm surge*? `3 marks`

48 Give an example of how coastal topography can contribute to the impact of storm surges. `4 marks`

49 Describe what is being done to a named island to reduce the risk of coastal flooding. `4 marks`

50 Explain why Bangladesh is at risk from severe coastal flooding. `6 marks`

51 Summarise FOUR of the predictions made about the physical impacts of global warming. 4 marks

....

....

....

....

....

52 Study Figure 11 which shows past, present and forecasted global sea levels.

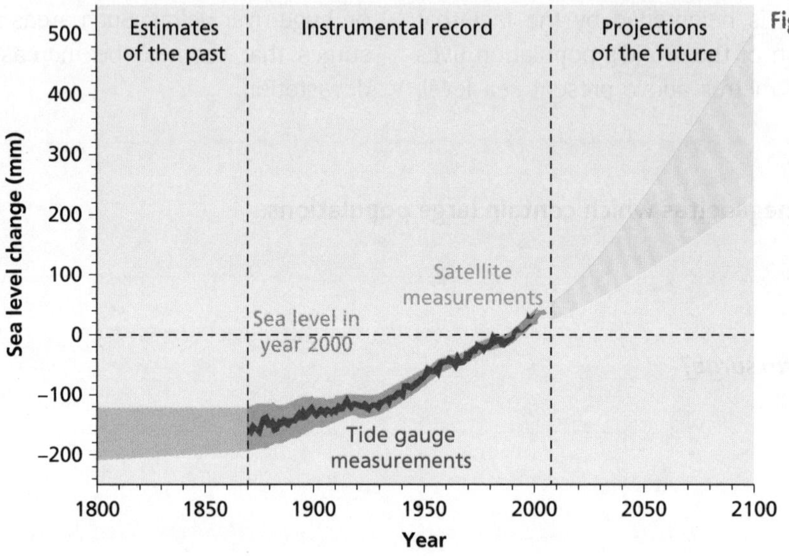

Figure 11

a   What do the estimates tell us about sea levels in the 1800–70 period? 2 marks

....

....

b   Describe what the instrumental record tells us about the twentieth century. 3 marks

....

....

....

....

c   What is the message about future projections? 3 marks

....

....

....

....

How can coastlines be managed to meet the needs of all players?

The consequences of coastal recession and flooding

The increased risks of coastal recession and coastal flooding threaten many communities with serious consequences. The losses resulting tend to be localised, while the costs are economic, social and environmental. In some parts of the world, the scale of recession and flooding are such as to soon require the wholesale abandonment of particularly low-lying islands and coastal zones. The prospect is one of growing numbers of environmental refugees fleeing a rising sea level.

53 Give examples of the economic and social losses resulting from coastal recession. `4 marks`

54 What are the main factors affecting the costs of coastal recession? `4 marks`

55 What sort of assessments would be made in an Environmental Impact Assessment (EIA) of a proposed sea defence project? `4 marks`

56 Do you agree that the consequences of coastal flooding are greater in developing countries? Give your reasons. `6 marks`

57 Explain what is meant by *environmental refugees*. `4 marks`

58 Give reasons why the island of Tuvalu is likely to be one of the first sources of environmental refugees. 6 marks

....

....

....

....

....

....

Approaches to managing coastal recession and flooding

There are at least three different approaches to managing the risks and threats associated with coastal recession and flooding: hard, soft and sustainable. While hard and soft engineering approaches are readily distinguishable, the last of these is less readily so. It depends on what is meant by 'sustainable'. It also depends on local circumstances. Generally speaking, sustainable management aims to protect the people of the coastal zone and their livelihoods in such a way as to minimise the ecological and environmental impacts of doing so.

59 What is involved in a *hard engineering* approach to coastal management? 3 marks

....

....

....

60 Why might some stakeholders object to a hard engineering approach? 4 marks

....

....

....

....

61 Explain what is involved in a *soft engineering* approach to coastal management. 4 marks

....

....

....

....

62 Do you agree that a soft engineering approach to coastal management is better than a hard engineering approach? Give your reasons. 4 marks

....

....

....

....

63 **What is meant by the terms *mitigation* and *adaptation*?** 4 marks

....

....

....

....

64 **Explain why sustainable coastal management can often lead to local conflicts.** 3 marks

....

....

....

Integrated Coastal Zone Management (ICZM)

Coastlines today are being increasingly managed in a holistic and integrated way that makes varying use of all three of the basic management approaches (hard, soft and sustainable). Coastal management is now planned on the basis of littoral cells. These are natural, self-contained subdivisions of the coast. For this reason they lend themselves to management as holistic units.

65 **Explain what is meant by *Integrated Coastal Zone Management* (ICZM).** 6 marks

....

....

....

....

....

....

....

....

66 **Identify FOUR different coastal management options.** 4 marks

....

....

....

....

67 **Name the main factors that are likely to influence the choice of coastal management option.** 3 marks

....

....

....

68 Illustrate the point that coastal management is most likely to involve decisions that will divide stakeholders into 'winners' and 'losers'. 6 marks

....

....

....

....

....

69 Is the need for coastal management any less in the developing world than the developed world? 6 marks

....

....

....

....

....

....

70 Study Figure 12 which gives some land value costs in England.

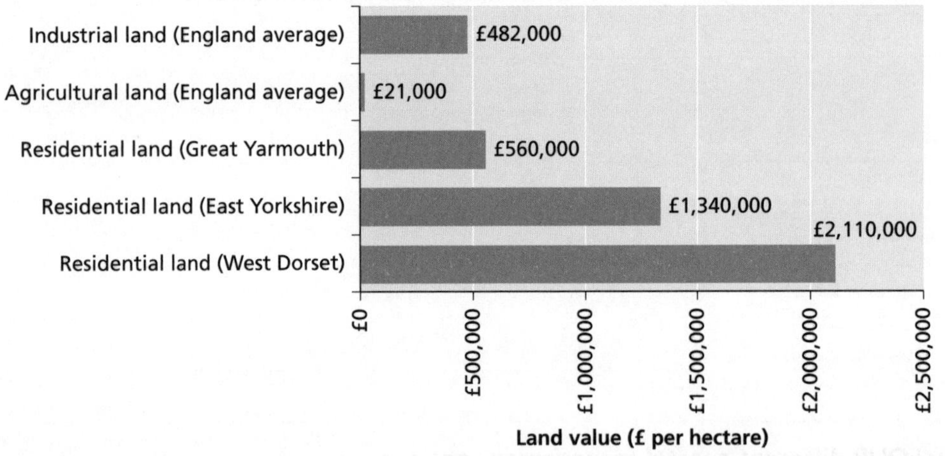

Land category	Land value (£ per hectare)
Industrial land (England average)	£482,000
Agricultural land (England average)	£21,000
Residential land (Great Yarmouth)	£560,000
Residential land (East Yorkshire)	£1,340,000
Residential land (West Dorset)	£2,110,000

Land value (£ per hectare)

Figure 12

Explain the possible impacts of these values where there is coastal recession. 6 marks

....

....

....

....

....

....

....

Exam-style questions

1 Study Figure 13 which shows the distribution of the annual rate of isostatic adjustment in Great Britain.

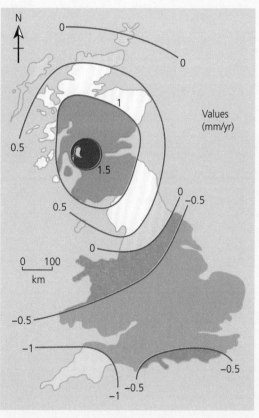

Figure 13

Values (mm/yr)

```
0   100
    km
```

a What is the maximum range in the annual rate? 2 **1 mark**

....

b Explain the coastal impacts of this pattern of isostatic adjustment. 6-8 **6 marks**

....

....

....

....

....

....

....

....

....

....

....

....

2 Explain the part played by longshore drift in the development of coastal landforms.

10-12 | 12 marks

3 Evaluate the statement that the main coastal threats are caused by nature rather than people.

25   **20 marks**

Also available

...and many more

Go to http://www.hoddereducation.co.uk/studentworkbooks for details of all our student workbooks.

Hodder Education, an Hachette UK company, Blenheim Court, George Street, Banbury, Oxfordshire OX16 5BH

Orders
Bookpoint Ltd, 130 Park Drive, Milton Park, Abingdon, Oxfordshire OX14 4SB

tel: 01235 827827
fax: 01235 400401
e-mail: education@bookpoint.co.uk

Lines are open 9.00 a.m.–5.00 p.m., Monday to Saturday, with a 24-hour message answering service.

You can also order through the Hodder Education website: www.hoddereducation.co.uk

© Michael Witherick 2017

ISBN 978-1-4718-8314-9

First printed 2017

Impression number   5   4   3   2
Year   2021 2020 2019 2018 2017

This guide has been written specifically to support students preparing for the Edexcel A-level Geography examinations. The content has been neither approved nor endorsed by Edexcel and remains the sole responsibility of the authors.

Photograph on page 33: duncanandison/Fotolia

Typeset by Aptara, India

Printed in Dubai

Hachette UK's policy is to use papers that are natural, renewable and recyclable products and made from wood grown in sustainable forests. The logging and manufacturing processes are expected to conform to the environmental regulations of the country of origin.

ISBN 978-1-4718-8314-9

9 781471 883149